CONTENTS

Learning Songs

Supplementary Songs

Series Editor: Mark Mumford

Music arranged and processed by Barnes Music Engraving Ltd
East Sussex TN22 4HA, England

Cover Design by Headline Publicity Ltd, Chelmsford, Essex

International Music Publications Limited
Griffin House 161 Hammersmith Road London W6 8BS England

INTRODUCTION

The Music About Us series aims to provide an essential library of topical resource material for Key Stage One and Key Stage Two pupils. The songs, together with the accompanying teaching ideas, are ideal for creating an immediate musical environment.

The Learning Songs are original, informative and fun to sing and perform. They provide thematic links to other subjects within the National Curriculum and will prove ideal for cross-curricular topic or project work. The use of the songs, and indeed much of the material in this series, will be dependent upon the age and ability of the children. In most cases however, the material is flexible enough to be adapted to deal with a number of requirements, thus providing the teacher with an ideal resource collection to 'dip into'.

Teaching Ideas provide initial suggestions for using the learning songs. They offer a variety of ways in which the songs may be performed, sometimes including ideas for actions, movement games and instrumental accompaniments. These suggestions can be combined to form a complete performance or simply selected to help with musical response and understanding. Their use will be dependent on key stage requirements.

The Musical Discussion notes offer further ideas and suggestions for exploring musical concepts. They provide initial points of discussion, sometimes concentrating on one specific musical element. There are many ways of developing these points but primarily they act as a basis for stimulating further work.

The Topical Discussion notes provide a series of leads enabling further exploration of the thematic content of the song. These are particularly useful for cross-curricular links within the National Curriculum, when applicable to the relevant key stage.

The Supplementary Song section offers a variety of songs, many of which may be well known. These songs may prove suitable for a number of uses, but as thematic material they can be used simply for singing. However, they can be developed by adding percussion accompaniments, actions etc.

Whether it is used to sing and learn about ourselves, how we live and the world around us, or as a basis for stimulating musical activity, the *Music About Us* series will undoubtedly prove a useful resource for music making in the classroom.

The Weather Forecast

Words and Music by
Carrie Morrow

4

In Scotland sleet and snow,
Wales will be wet and windy.
In Ireland ice, and raining very fast,
And for England, what is the weather forecast?

In the North, no sun, only hail.
In the West, wild winds blow a gale.
Showers further south, and the East even wetter,
And tomorrow's forecast isn't any better.

TEACHING IDEAS

A song about the weather forecast.

Actions

In the 2nd verse children should point North, West, South and East.

Accompaniments

Sound Effects:

Snow – Use a cymbal with a soft beater
Wind – Softly blowing a whistle
Rain – Short tapping sounds on drums
Hail – Sharper tapping sounds using claves

Musical Discussion

Draw some weather symbols, on cards, which might be seen on a typical television weather forecast. Using percussion sounds to match the symbols, ask the children to compose their own 'Weather Forecast Song'.

For example:

| Sunshine | Rain | Sleet | Thunderstorm | Snow | Rain with sunny intervals |

When the weather elements are mixed, e.g. *Sleet*, then a combination of percussion sounds should be used. Ask a group to perform their piece. Can the other children identify the different types of weather?

Compare rhythms of the countries mentioned in the song.

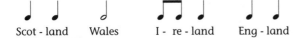

Which two have the same rhythm? What other countries can the children think of and match rhythmic patterns to? Ask the children to imitate the rhythm using percussion instruments.

Topical Discussion

What is a weather forecast? Why do we need them? How important are they (e.g. for farmers)? Discuss other ways in which we could forecast the weather. Do the children know of any 'old sayings'? What does it mean when cows lie down? Name the four points of a compass. Does the weather change much from day to day? Find out by keeping a weather diary.

Discuss how weather makes you feel sad or happy. This song is about quite gloomy weather. Give a weather forecast for bright, cheerful weather.

Radiating Rays

Words and Music by
Carrie Morrow

1 Nearer to the sun the equator is hot,
   Further from the heat, the poles, they are not.
   Less solar, more polar,
   Less solar, more polar.

   Dress in black instead of white,
   Absorbing the sunlight.
   Dress in white instead of black,
   Reflecting those rays right back.

2 Ice-cream melts in radiating rays,
   Sweating, we lose heat on hot sunny days.
   Burning fire warm the air,
   Burning fire warm the air.
        Dress in black . . .

TEACHING IDEAS

A song about the sun and how it affects us.

Actions

Absorb the light – Close arms to the body
Reflect the rays – Spread arms and fingers out wide

Accompaniments

This piece has a *calypso* feel about it, so try to use percussion instruments that reflect this.

Bars 1–4 and 9–16

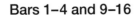 Shakers, coconut shells, drums with soft beaters etc.

Bars 4–8

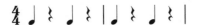 Xylophone

Musical Discussion

Introduce the rhythm of the title – *Radiating Rays*, and ask the children to clap it and say it at the same time. Then ask them to think up an 'answer' with the same rhythm.

For example:

Ra - di - at - ing rays   Answer: Shi - ning down on me.

Discuss the instruments the children used in this song. Can they make their own? Choose a recording of a folk song from a hot country such as Jamaica, and one from a colder country like Scotland. Discuss the differences. Talk about the different instruments that are used. Are there any words to the songs? What are they about?

Topical Discussion

What is the sun? How does the sun affect our weather? Explain how heat from the sun travels to the Earth as rays by *radiation*. How do we measure temperature? Which countries have very hot weather? Why are these countries hotter? Explain why shadows change size and move throughout the day. Why are houses in very hot countries sometimes painted white? What does our body do when it gets too hot? What energy do we get from the sun? Discuss the dangers of being out in the sun too long.

Freeze

Words and Music by
Carrie Morrow

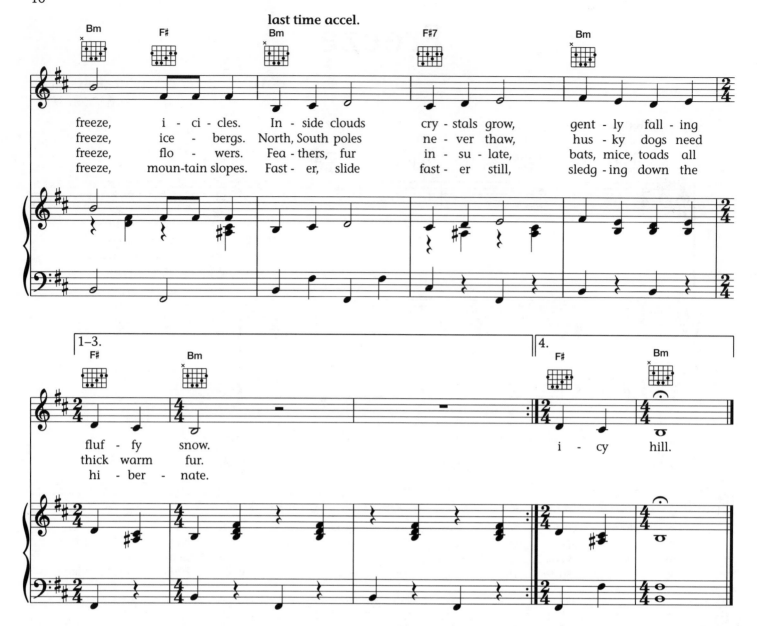

1 Cold clear nights,
   No clouds cover
   Frosty sights,
   White all over.
   Freeze, feathered frost,
   Freeze, icicles,
   Freeze, feathered frost,
   Freeze, icicles.
   Inside clouds crystals grow,
   Gently falling fluffy snow.

2 Frozen land,
   Arctic ice age,
   Polar bears,
   Fierce ice rage.
   Freeze, glaciers,
   Freeze, icebergs,
   Freeze, glaciers,
   Freeze, icebergs.
   North, South poles never thaw,
   Husky dogs need thick warm fur.

3 Creatures, plants,
   Must survive,
   Food and heat
   Keeps them alive.
   Freeze, animals,
   Freeze, flowers,
   Freeze, animals,
   Freeze, flowers.
   Feathers, fur insulate,
   Bats, mice, toads all hibernate.

4 Sport is fun
   On ice, on snow.
   Clip on skis,
   Whizzing we go.
   Freeze, ice-rink,
   Freeze, mountain slopes,
   Freeze, ice-rink,
   Freeze, mountain slopes.
   Faster, slide faster still
   Sledging down the icy hill.

TEACHING IDEAS

A song describing what happens when everything is frozen.

Actions

If possible the children should walk around in a large circle. On the word 'freeze' they should create a body shape and stand still.

Accompaniments

Bars 3–6

 Soft beating on drums

On the word 'freeze' strike a triangle.

This song is quite atmospheric, ask the children to whisper the word 'freeze'.

Musical Discussion

Discuss the musical atmosphere of this song and relate it to night time. Why did the music get faster at the end of the last verse? Ask the children what else freezes. Can they fit their answers to the beat of the 'freeze' bar?

For example:

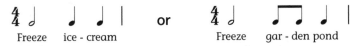

Ask the children to compose an icicle score by drawing a row of icicles. The longer the icicle the lower the sound should be. By adding drops of water under each icicle the children can decide how many times to repeat the sound. Let them perform, compose and record their results. This can be made more challenging by changing the icicle to the notes of a scale and the water drops to represent beats.

Topical Discussion

Why is it colder on clear nights? What is the difference between frost and ice? What differences are there between countries that are always covered in ice or snow and our own country? How is the wildlife different? How do people dress and how do they travel? Discuss winter sports and make a list of different activities. Have the children tried any of them? Ask them to describe how each sport is performed. Discuss snow flakes – why is each one different? Why should we be careful in cold weather?

The Water Cycle

Words and Music by
Carrie Morrow

1   The sun shines down,
     The water rises up.
     What a sensation, (*clap*)
     Evaporation!

       Riding, riding, riding in the sky,
       As the clouds drift by.
       Riding, riding, riding round and round on a (*clap*)
       Water cycle.

2   The water cools down,
     The clouds fill up.
     What a sensation, (*clap*)
     Condensation!
       Riding, riding, riding . . .

3   Raindrops fall down,
     Umbrellas go up.
     What a sensation, (*clap*)
     Precipitation!
       Riding, riding, riding . . .

4   The sun shines down,
     The water rises up.
     What a sensation, (*clap*)
     Evaporation! (*clap*)
     Condensation! (*clap*)
     Precipitation!
     The wonder of all creation.

TEACHING IDEAS

A song that helps to explain where rain comes from.

Actions

Ask the children to point up and down throughout the verses as the words dictate. During the chorus pretend to be riding up and down on a bicycle.

Accompaniments

Clap hands as marked in the score.

For example:

(clap) E - va - po - ra - tion!

Alternatively a 'clash' of cymbals could be used here. *'What a sensation, evaporation'* – these words should be sung loudly in each verse.

 Tambourines

What a sen - sa - tion

Chorus

 Alternate with recorders, glocks and xylophones

Musical Discussion

Ask the children to describe the sound that rain makes. How does it sound when it lands in a puddle? How does it sound when it hits a window pane? Discuss the different speeds at which rain falls. Play a movement game using words that describe different types of rain fall.

For example:

Slow   –   little drops
Walking speed   –   light shower
Running   –   cloud burst

Choose a leader to call out the instructions and ask the children to react by moving. Ask them to think about loud and quiet as well.

Ask the children to compose their own 'rainy day' piece. Encourage them to create three sections in their piece. Section A should represent the beginning of the rain which should build up to Section B – the rain storm. Section C should be Section A reversed. For younger children, use percussion instruments with each child introducing his or her own sound effect until all are playing during the storm. Each child gradually drops out during Section C. Encourage older children to use tuned instruments with rhythmic values. Ask the children to discuss the performance with particular reference to graduations of speed, dynamics and texture.

Topical Discussion

Explain the *water cycle*. What does the word *cycle* mean? What other types of *cycles* do the children know? Where does rain come from? If it comes from the sea, why is it never salty? Explain how wind and warmth make water evaporate, e.g. clothes drying on a washing line. What happens when a kettle boils? What happens when you breathe out air on a cold day? What does *precipitation* mean? Explain that air gets cooler as it rises and that the water droplets in the air condense, get bigger and gather to make clouds. When does the water fall as rain? Discuss the journey of water from when it falls as rain to when it comes out of our taps at home. Discuss different cloud names. Which clouds are more likely to mean it's going to rain?

Weather Warning

Words and Music by
Carrie Morrow

1 Hurricanes, typhoons, winds that spin,
   Devastate land and suck you in.
   Tornadoes tear down house and tree,
   Out of the way, wind energy!
      Wind can be dangerous
      Wind can be dangerous
      See the dangers of the wind!

2 Over the sea wall waves are blown,
   Rivers burst banks floods can drown.
   Dangerous, deep now look and see,
   Gasping for air the tallest tree.
      Floods can be dangerous,
      Floods can be dangerous,
      See the dangers of the floods!

3 Electric flashing thunder cloud,
   Burning touch angry and loud.
   Lightning strikes at church spires tall,
   Flashing clapping branches fall.
      Storms can be dangerous,
      Storms can be dangerous,
      See the dangers of the storms!

4 The weather is frosty, some advice,
   Drive with care, invisible black ice.
   Suddenly stop, brakes try to grip,
   Traffic collides as tyres just slip.
      Ice can be dangerous,
      Ice can be dangerous,
      See the dangers of the ice!

TEACHING IDEAS

A song describing how weather can sometimes be powerful and dangerous.

Actions

Verses

Winds that spin	–	Jump and turn
Waves are blown	–	Raise and lower arms
Thunder cloud	–	Stamp on floor
Some advice	–	Finger warning action

Accompaniments

Verse

Repeat this rhythm throughout each verse. Change percussion instruments to reflect different weather.

Alternatively, sound effects could be used:

Verse 1	–	Panpipes or other wind instruments (getting louder and quieter)
Verse 2	–	Chordal sounds on xylophones
Verse 3	–	Drum rolls ending with a cymbal clash
Verse 4	–	A glissando on glocks

Musical Discussion

Look at all of the different types of weather that are mentioned in the song and discuss what they sound like. Talk about the sounds, particularly gradation of speed and dynamics. Ask the children to imitate using percussion instruments. Ask other children to move in response to the dynamics i.e. crouching and growing as the sounds get quieter and louder. Can they draw signs to illustrate the dynamics? How would somebody 'conduct' getting louder and softer? Ask the children to write a poem about the weather which includes a thunderstorm. Ask them to work out sound effects to go with their poem. Do the sounds ever combine?

Choose some rhythms that go with various words in the song. Divide the children into groups giving each group a chant. Group one starts by chanting four times, then the second and then the third. Percussion instruments or clapping could also be used.

For example:

Topical Discussion

Explain that winds are named after the direction they come from. Powerful winds are given other names. Can the children name three powerful winds? (The answers are in the song!) How can we measure the direction of the wind? How is wind speed measured? What causes flooding? What causes thunder and lightning? Why do we hear thunder sometimes after we see the lightning? Why are thunder storms sometimes called *electric storms?* Weather can be powerful and sometimes dangerous. Discuss the effects of dangerous weather. Talk about different countries around the world which are particularly at risk from dangerous weather.

Atmos-Fear

Words and Music by
Carrie Morrow

1   Earth in space shines green and blue,
     Thick pollution clouds the view,
     Gasp to breathe in air that's clear;
     What is choking the atmosphere?

2   Pollution puffed from chimneys tall,
     Clouds spitting acid rainfall.
     A burning, poisoned, killing rain,
     Stop! Make flowers grow again.

3   Exhaust fumes, gases mix with smoke,
     Don't breathe deep or you might choke.
     Round houses, factories, creeps this smog,
     Where is winter's pure white fog?

4   Poisoned weather, what is the solution
     To the problem of pollution?
     Take care of the air and keep it clean,
     Leave our planet healthy and green.

TEACHING IDEAS

A song describing the effects of pollution in our atmosphere.

Accompaniments

Throughout the verses, one group of children can whisper the following:

Verse 1:
Thick pol - lu - tion

Verse 2:
A - cid rain, A - cid rain

Verse 3:
Creep - ing smog

Verse 4:
Keep it clean

Verses

Xylophones

Musical Discussion

Ask the children to describe the mood of this piece. Why does it sound sad and solemn? Discuss why sounds can create different atmospheres. Talk about major and minor keys. What other sad music can the children think of? What happy music can they think of? Ask the children to paint a happy picture using bright colours and a sad one using dull and drab colours. What sounds would they add to each picture? Talk about how music affects us. Can it change our emotions? Can the children think of any examples of film or television themes, where music creates an atmosphere?

Topical Discussion

In this song ask the children to paint pictures to represent the different verses. Explain the meaning of *atmosphere*. Why is it spelt differently in the song? What causes pollution in our atmosphere? What are the effects of pollution? Discuss what is happening in other countries. How can we reduce pollution? How can we save energy? Ask the children to name some organisations that have been formed to help prevent pollution. Ask the children to design a poster to campaign against pollution in their local area.

Sing A Rainbow

Words and Music by
Arthur Hamilton

Red and yel-low and pink and green,

pur-ple and o-range and blue.

Red and yellow and pink and green,
Purple and orange and blue.
I can sing a rainbow,
Sing a rainbow,
Sing a rainbow too.

Listen with your eyes,
Listen with your eyes,
And sing everything you see.
You can sing a rainbow,
Sing a rainbow,
Sing along with me.

Red and yellow and pink and green,
Purple and orange and blue.
Now we can sing a rainbow,
Sing a rainbow,
Sing a rainbow too.

A favourite song with children, which works well as an introduction to linking colour with music.

Let It Snow, Let It Snow, Let It Snow

Words by Sammy Cahn
Music by Jule Styne

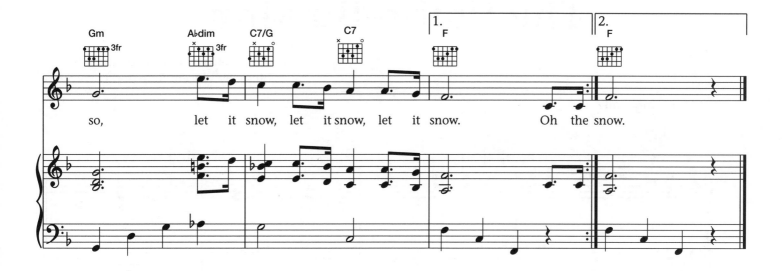

so,   let   it snow, let it snow, let   it snow.   Oh   the snow.

The snowman in the yard is frozen hard,
He's a sorry sight to see.
If he had a brain he'd complain,
Bet he wishes he were me.

Oh the weather outside is frightful.
But the fire is so delightful,
And since we've no place to go,
Let it snow, let it snow, let it snow.

It doesn't show signs of stopping,
And I brought some corn for popping,
The lights are turned way down low,
Let it snow, let it snow, let it snow.

When we finally kiss goodnight,
How I'll hate going out in the storm,
But if you really hold me tight,
All the way home I'll be warm.

The fire is slowly dying,
And my dear we're still goodbyeing,
But as long as you love me so,
Let it snow, let it snow, let it snow.

A favourite seasonal song. Try adding soft and light sounding percussion instruments to create the impression of falling snow.

The Umbrella Man

Words by James Cavanaugh
Music by Vincent Rose and Larry Stock

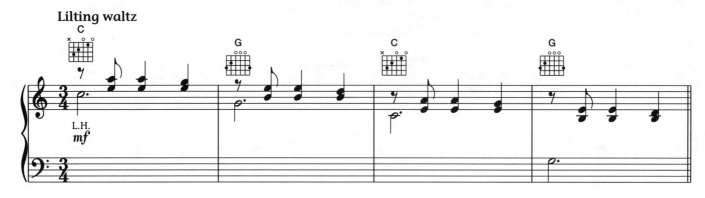

Too - dle - lum - a - lum - a, too - dle - lum - a - lum - a, too - dle - i -

- ay, a - ny um - be - rel - las, a - ny um - be - rel - las

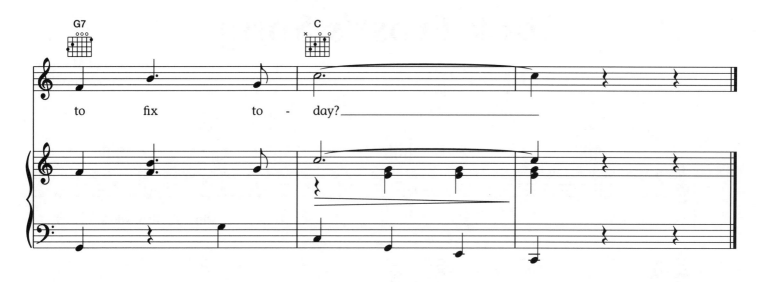

to fix to - day?_____

Toodle-lum-a-lum-a,
Toodle-lum-a-lum-a,
Toodle-i-ay,
Any umbrellas,
Any umbrellas to fix today?
Bring your parasol,
It may be small,
It may be big,
He repairs them all
With what you call a 'thingumajig'.

Pitter patter patter,
Pitter patter patter,
It looks like rain.
Let it pitter patter,
Let it pitter patter,
Don't mind the rain.
He'll mend your umbrella,
Then go on his way, singing
Toodle-lum-a-lum-a,
Toodle-ay,
Toodle-lum-a-lum-a,
Toodle-ay,
Any umbrellas to fix today?

A useful song with opportunities for sound effects and rhythmic training.

Jack Frost's Song

Words and Music by
Peter Canwell

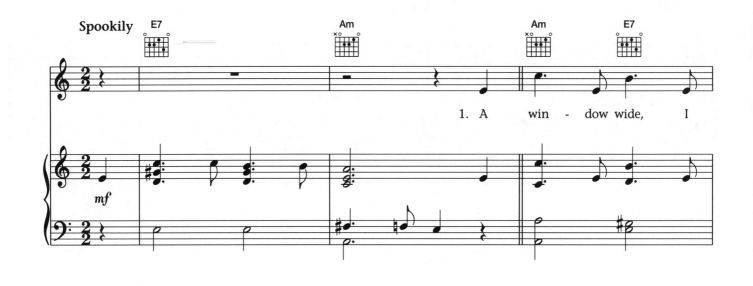

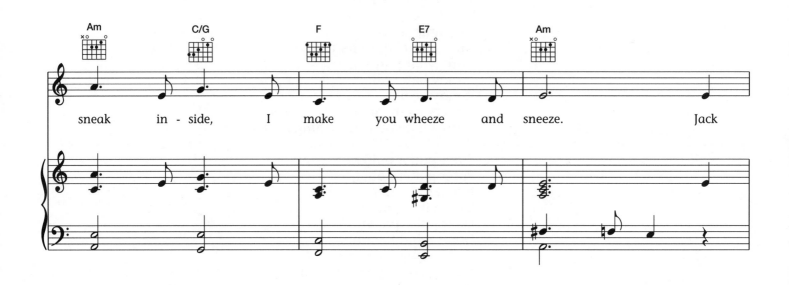

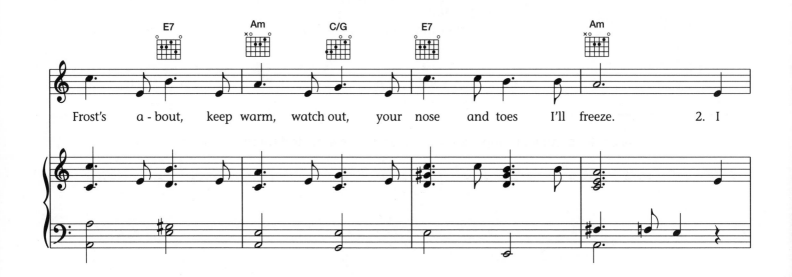

1   A window wide, I sneak inside,
     I make you wheeze and sneeze.
     Jack Frost's about,
     Keep warm, watch out,
     Your nose and toes I'll freeze.

2   I breathe on everything in sight,
     I paint your windows white.
     Jack Frost's about.
     Keep warm, watch out,
     'Cause I'll be back tonight,
     Yes, I'll be back tonight!
     Yes, I'll be back tonight!

An ideal song for incorporating actions.

Whirlwind

Words and Music by
Stan Jones

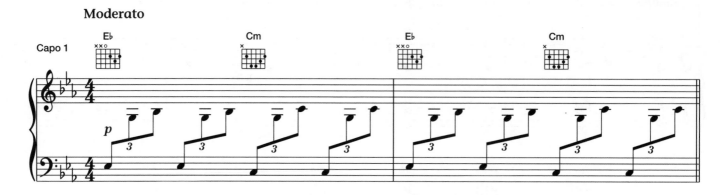

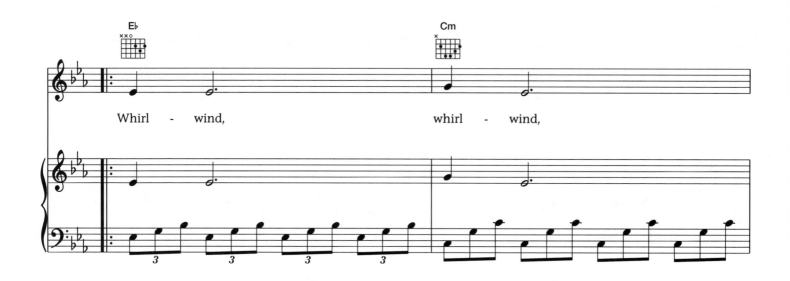

Whirl - wind, whirl - wind,

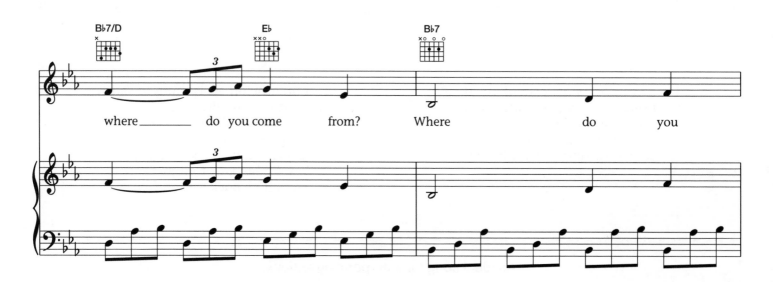

where _____ do you come from? Where do you

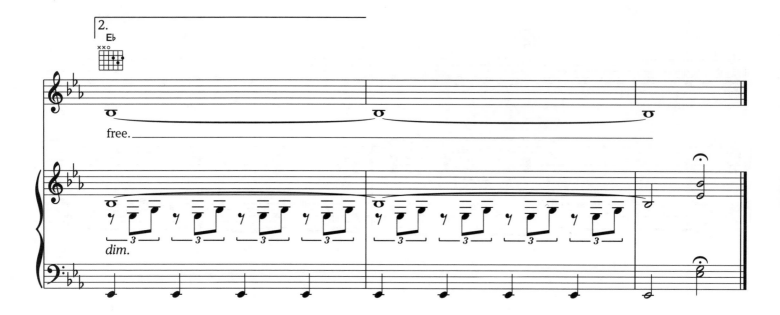

free.

dim.

Whirlwind, whirlwind,
Where do you come from?
Where do you go?
Whirlwind, whirlwind,
Around so fast,
Along so slow.

Whirly, whirly,
Will-o-the-wisp,
Enchanted spire,
Sunlight kissed.

Whirlwind, whirlwind,
Never caring,
With earth and sky
Your love a-sharing.
All that matters,
Just like me,
Is just to roam at will so free.

A good movement song with opportunities for adding sound effects.

With The Sun Warm Upon Me

Words by Dorothy Fields
Music by Harold Arlen

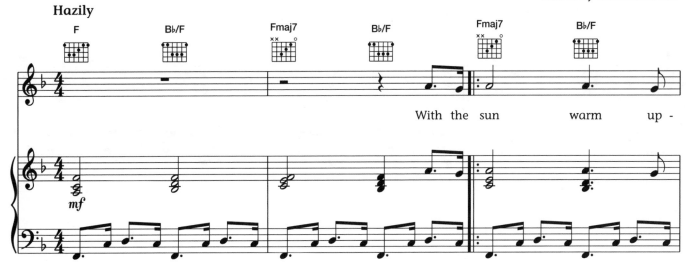

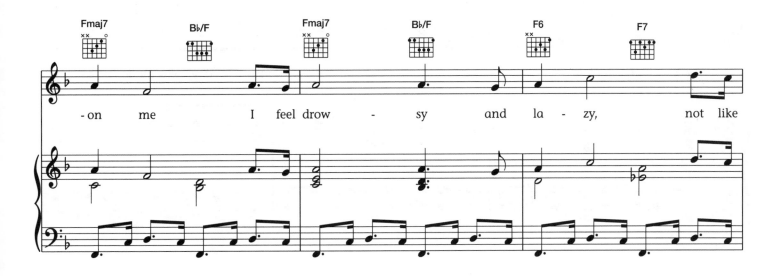

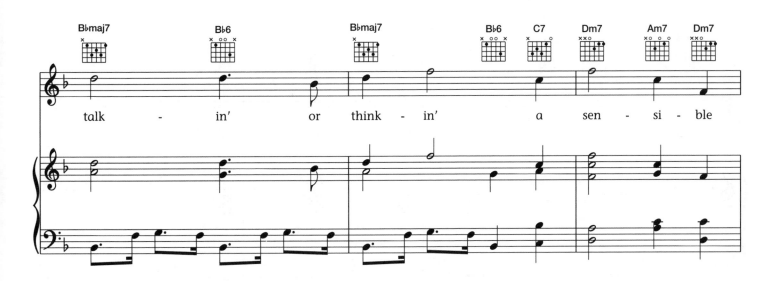

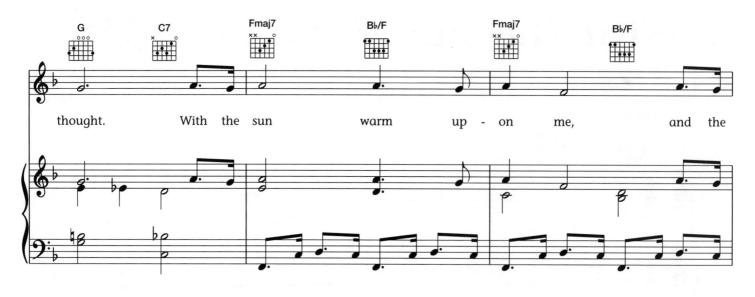

thought.   With the sun   warm   up - on me,   and the

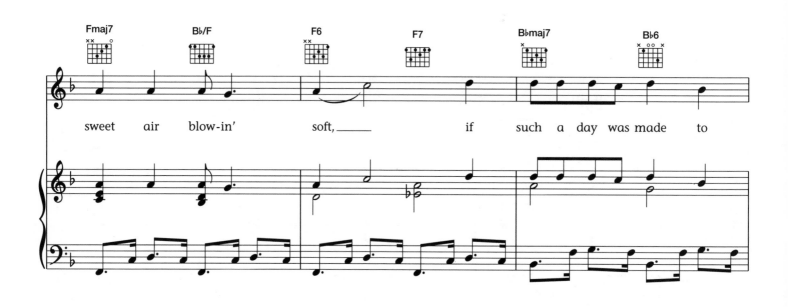

sweet air blow-in'   soft, _____   if   such a day was made to

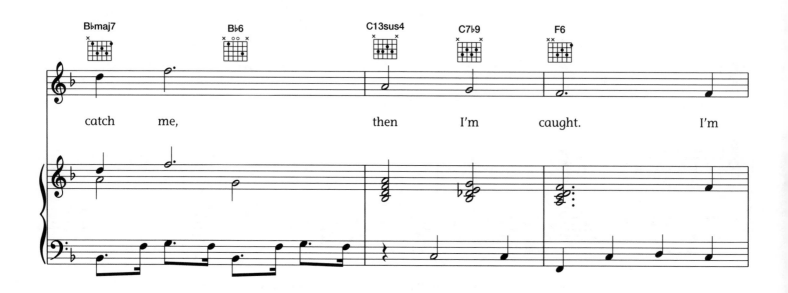

catch   me,   then   I'm   caught.   I'm

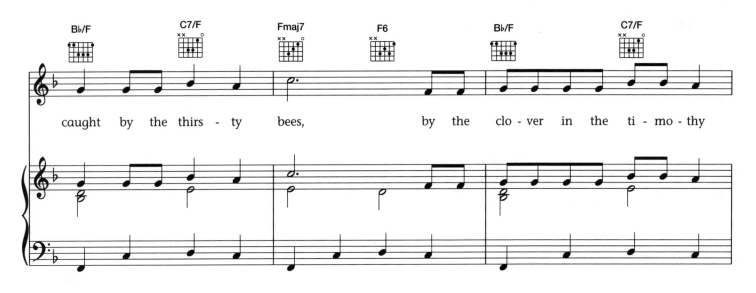

caught by the thirs - ty bees, by the clo - ver in the ti - mo - thy

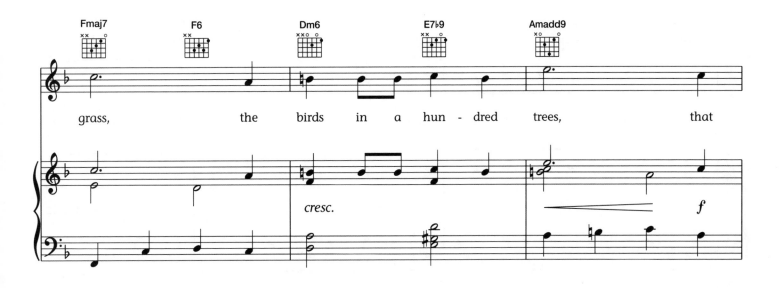

grass, the birds in a hun - dred trees, that

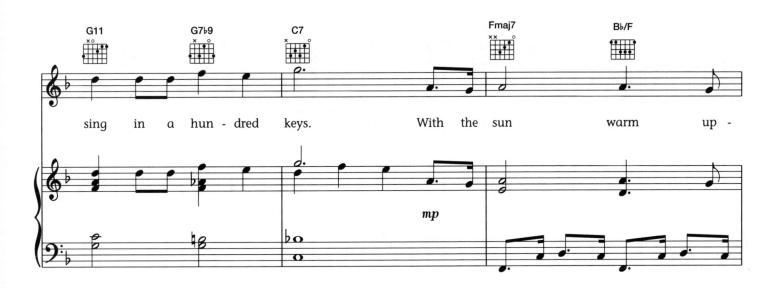

sing in a hun - dred keys. With the sun warm up -

-on me   there's no time,   there's   no   space,___   there's

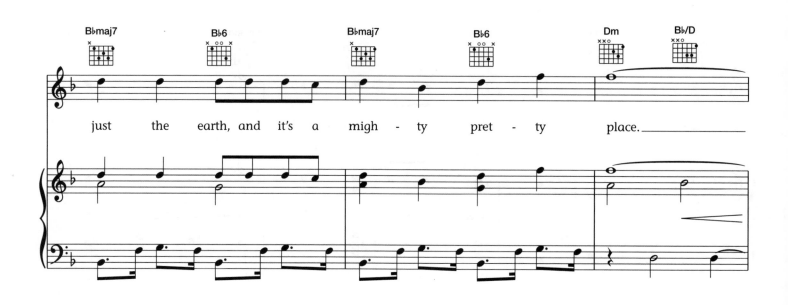

just   the   earth, and   it's   a   migh - ty   pret - ty   place._____

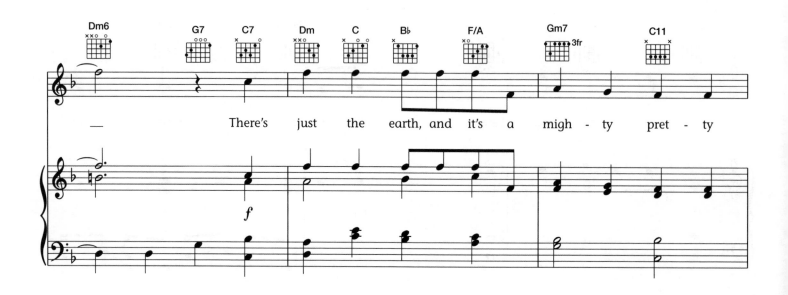

There's   just   the   earth, and   it's   a   migh - ty   pret - ty

place._____ With the _____

With the sun warm upon me I feel drowsy and lazy,
Not like talkin' or thinkin' a sensible thought.
With the sun warm upon me and the sweet air blowin' soft,
If such a day was made to catch me then I'm caught.

I'm caught by the thirsty bees,
By the clover in the timothy grass,
The birds in a hundred trees,
That sing in a hundred keys.

With the sun warm upon me there's no time, there's no space
There's just the earth, and it's a mighty pretty place,
There's just the earth, and it's a mighty pretty place.

A song that provides useful discussion about how the weather affects our moods.

Little April Shower

Words by Larry Morey
Music by Frank Churchill

I never mind how much it rains in April,
I never lose my temper and complain.
If you come down my way on any rainy day,
You'll always hear me singing in the rain.

Drip drip drop, little April shower,
Beating a tune as you fall all around.
Drip drip drop, little April shower,
What can compare with your beautiful sound?

Drip drip drop when the sky is cloudy,
Your pretty music can brighten the day.
Drip drip drop when the sun says 'Howdy',
You say 'Goodbye' right away.

Drip drip drop, little April shower,
Beating a tune everywhere that you fall.
Drip drip drop, little April shower,
I'm getting wet and I don't care at all.

Drip! Drop! Drip! Drop!
I'll never be afraid of a good little,
Gay little April serenade.

Lots of opportunities here for adding percussion accompaniments. Use the four bar phrases that start 'Drip, drip, drop little . . .' to explore getting louder and quieter.

1/00

Printed by
Halstan & Co. Ltd., Amersham, Bucks., England

Songs, activities and music & movement to excite and enthuse the very young

All these books are ideal for Pre-school and Key Stage 1 and are arranged for easy piano with guitar chords.

Niki Davies

6325A　　　**£9.99**
It's Time To Wake Up

6326A　　　**£9.99**
I'm Walking Down The Street

6323A　　　**£9.99**
Everything's Growing

6324A　　　**£9.99**
What's The Difference?

- 12 simple and catchy tunes in each book which draw on the experiences of 3-7 year olds
- Explore the use of home made percussion and free flowing movement to develop children's concentration and listening skills
- Experience the excitement of producing a mini-musical
- Full demonstration and backing track versions of the songs as well as descriptive music and sounds for acting, moving and miming are included on the CD

'The choice of themes for these collections and the material they contain is commendable … the attractively arranged accompaniments on the CDs make the collections accessible all teachers, whether or not they have instrumental skills. [These books] show the composer's obvious understanding of working with young children.' Music Teacher, October 199

New! Class Act Productions

- Two brand new musicals which your pupils will love to be a part of, from the writers that brought you 'Around The World In A Thousand Years'
- Two tracks on the CD: one with children's voices for rehearsals, the other without for the end performance
- Gives essential hints and tips on staging, use of costumes, choreography and scheduling rehearsals
- Everything you need is here to ensure a hassle free production. Together with your free publicity pack, it will look like you spent the whole year getting it right - but you and the kids will know different!

6524A　　　**£12.99**
Little Red Hen (A Farmyard Fable)

6523A　　　**£12.99**
The Shiniest Star (A Nativity)

International MUSIC Publications

International Music Publications Ltd.
Griffin House, 161 Hammersmith Road,
Hammersmith, London W6 8BS

Buy these titles from your local music shop, or contact:

MUSIC MAIL
Print, Video & Education Specialists
A Warner Music Group Company

FREEPHONE 0800 376 9101
International Telephone: +44 20 8222 9232
Facsimile: 020 8222 9260
Email: Music_Mail@warnerchappell.com